ENERGY ON A PLATE

**All recipes free from
dairy products, wheat, yeast, sugar
and salt.**

**Coeliacs, hypoglycaemics, candida sufferers
and all who wish to follow a
healthy lifestyle using natural ingredients
may find interesting recipes to help
with restrictive diets.**

LIZEE MCGRAW

Illustrated by Fiona Munn

Linton Associates, Dunblane, Scotland

Published in Scotland by
Linton Associates
Wanaka Lodge, Dunblane, FK15 0JU

A catalogue record for this book is available from the British Library

ISBN 0-9537556-0-6

Printed in Scotland by
The University of Edinburgh Printing Services

Foreword

Lizee McGraw D.N.Med. D.Iridol.

Member of the British Association of Nutritional Therapists

Lizee McGraw's own glowing vitality is radiant tribute to her enthusiasm for healthy nutrition. Her life-long interest led her on to explore recipes that liberate our energies and delight our tastebuds. Eating for energy and health was a guiding principle she first learnt from her mother when as a child she watched and helped at home in the kitchen. Lizee's flare with food encouraged her to train in cookery with City and Guilds.

Lizee travelled the world, living in both Canada and Australia before settling in Scotland. Balanced nutrition and exercise have been a pivotal influence in her life. Having successfully worked with her husband to establish a family business, she turned her energies to the study of nutrition and discovered scientific reasons for her abiding belief that the way we eat can nourish the body and spirit.

As a qualified nutritionist, she now combines her busy Nutritinal Medicine Practice with cookery demonstrations for people eager to learn more about preparing delicious dishes with wholesome, life-enhancing ingredients. The popularity of the "cook-ins" in her own kitchen and further afield encouraged Lizee to develop her collection of refreshing recipes which are lucidly explained in this book.

by Jenny Rutty

Introduction

Welcome to your new way of eating. This book is for people seeking a way to enhance their life with positive, healthy nourishment - not just eating through jaded habit or because it is time to 'refuel' with a meal. Feel the goodness not only in the eating but in the cooking of these revitalising meals. The recipes are free from wheat, dairy, sugar and yeast products and better still there are many ingredients which will be new to you, full of bountiful nutrients to assist the body to balance and respond healthily to aid growth and repair tissues. If you do not have all the ingredients suggested then feel free to make adjustments. Vegetables are particularly interchangeable. You will find it exciting and relaxing to experiment with flavours. The whole purpose is to use food for health.

As you use these recipes you will find your taste buds alter and you will demand different flavours. Where possible use organic products and happily you will find that a bigger range is becoming far more widely available. Remember that your protein will be coming from pulses, nuts, fish, beans and seeds. To complete the protein when eating pulses and beans make sure rice, buckwheat or millet is taken at the same meal. It is important to consume a good percentage of raw salads and vegetables. Try to prepare these just before eating them so that their nutrient value is not dispersed.

It is essential that we have effective elimination of waste products from our gut but if we eat unhealthily then a build up of poor bacteria and stale substances accumulate which in turn promotes further difficulties in our personal 'engines'. Among the many advantages of renewing your eating pattern with health-giving food is the increased level of energy and feeling of spiritual, mental and physical harmony it promotes.

This book has been written because so many of my clients who needed alternative ingredients could not find suitable recipes. I hope you too will enjoy these recipes and share the abundant sense of well-being that I have experienced in devising, preparing and relishing tasty meals using good food.

Sprouting

Sprouted beans, pulses and seeds are probably one of the most exciting foods we eat. Children are fascinated by their fast production - overnight there is so much activity that natural impatience is quickly rewarded.

Another wonder of nature is performed with sprouting because the same seed would need to be soaked and boiled to kill off harmful chemicals if the food were being cooked but because it is eaten raw once it has sprouted the property of the seed is changed.

The reserves of energy which have been dormant in the seed are freed and made readily available to us. Enormous enzyme release gives us exceptional nutrtional quality from sprouts. The sprouting action breaks down stored starch which then turns into natural sugars. Proteins are split down into amino acids which are easily assimilated in the body. The nutrional value of sprouts is as high as any natural food giving abundant amounts of vitamins and minerals. The plant enzymes released should help to enhance the body's own system and assist in metabolizing oils and fats.

Grains

Grains are used all over the world as a staple part of the everyday diet. They are extremely important as their composition of both protein and carbohydrate complements other foods which are also made up of varying amounts of both. Seeds, pulses and nuts combined with grains round up the complete protein and give us the essential amino acids in one meal. Grains have valuable nutritional contents including calcium, iron, zinc and the B vitamins. Natural, organic grains are very rich in fibre which is essential for our digestive system. Many people are not accustomed to cooking with grains but once you have experimented with them they become a simple and essential part of a meal. Flavour them with herbs and spices to your individual taste. Below is a guide for cooking grains.

Grain	Water	Cooking time	Pressure cooker
Brown rice - 1 cup	2 cups	30 mins	10 mins
Buckwheat - 1 cup	2 cups	20 mins	8 mins
Millet - 1 cup	3 cups	30 mins	8 mins

If you prefer to bring the grain in its water to the boil and then place it in a moderate oven then it will take approximately the same length of time mentioned and will be cooked to perfection.

Pulses

Pulses are so versatile - adding particular texture to stews, casseroles and soups and they are an amazingly economical ingredient. Soak dried beans overnight to help eliminate gas producing sugars and to reduce cooking time. Cook a good quantity and store them in the freezer ready for making main dishes. If you have a stainless steel pressure cooker it cuts down the cooking time considerably and does not fuzz up the kitchen with all that condensation! Most varieties of beans and lentils can be cooked in up to 15 mins by this method. Once the beans are cooked, throw away the water. Lentils do not need to be soaked overnight and their water may be used in soups and casseroles. The cooking time usually consists of boiling for the first 10-15 mins (which creates all the steam) and then reduce to a simmer for the next hour or however long it takes the particular bean to become soft.

Type	Soak	Cooking Time	Pressure Cooker
Black Eyed	overnight	2 hours	15 mins
Butterbeans	overnight	$1^1/_2$ hour	20 mins
Chickpeas	overnight	$1^1/_2$ hours	10-12 mins
Flagelot	overnight	$2^1/_2$ hours	10-12 mins
Haricot	overnight	50 mins	20 mins
Kidney	overnight	$1^1/_2$ hours	10-12 mins
Lentils	No	45 mins	15 mins
Split Peas	No	1 hour	15 mins

Most of these will be pre cooked and will have more cooking time when added to casseroles, soups or stews.

Weights & Measures

It is sometimes confusing if recipes are written in grams and you prefer to weigh things in ounces so I have given a comparison table to avoid mistakes. Wherever I have used a cup - this is a traditional tea cup and certainly takes the mystic out of weighing ingredients.

grams (g)	ounces (oz)
15	1/2
30	1
60	2
90	3
125	4
155	5
185	6

For quick measurements of liquids I find spoons helpful and work on the guide of a teaspoon = 5 ml. a dessertspoon = 10 ml. a tablespoon = 20 ml.

Oven Temperatures

	C	F	Gas
Very cool	110	225	$^1/_4$
	120	250	$^1/_2$
Cool	140	275	1
	150	300	2
Moderate	160	325	3
	180	350	4
Moderately Hot	190	375	5
	200	400	6
Hot	220	425	7
	230	450	8
Very Hot	240	475	9

Fan assisted ovens generally require a slight reduction in cooking time and temperature.

BREADS, PASTRY & BREAKFAST

"I don't eat breakfast" is the response from many people who are dashing out to work, school or play having overslept. The most important start to the day is something to break the overnight 'fast' before we embark on a day's activities. The suggested use of fruits or grains and seeds are just what your body needs to swing smoothly into action first thing in the morning.
Although an important meal breakfast should be light because our body's systems are still working on elimination and digestion takes up a lot of energy. It is important that elimination is effected and that digestion of new food does not overtake this process.

The Breads are unconventional, from a Western viewpoint and make meals interesting and exciting. They are not vehicles for smearing with butter and jam but more flat breads to accompany main courses.

The alternative pastry, pie crust and pancakes are so helpful when feeding young people.

Corn Bread

serves 6-8

This is not conventional bread but rather more like a cake. I have had guests who have thought they were getting 'sponge cake' with their main meal. It is a very flexible accompaniment.

8 oz corn, polenta or maize flour
3 oz Potato flour
2 teaspoons Potassium baking powder
1 free range organic egg
$^1/_4$ pt rice milk
20 ml olive oil
1 fresh sweet corn or small can sweet corn
chopped chives

Grease a square 9 inch tin

Mix up all ingredients in a food mixer -
make sure it is pretty wet and add more water if necessary
pour into tin and bake in hot oven for about 25 mins.
The consistency of this mixture is very sloppy, similar to runny custard, unlike a conventional bread dough but the moisture will disappear with cooking and the cake like presentation is very satisfactory.

Serve with stews, casseroles or soups for 'dipping' in the traditional mid Eastern manner.

As an alternative fresh or dried chillies would give this bread a good kick.

Onion & Herb Bread

serves 6

This can accompany any main meal. It is not conventional 'bread' for spreading things on but more a middle eastern style bread for adding to stews, casseroles and salads. It is a sloppy mixture and literally has to be poured into the tin but the moisture is cooked out of it to form a baked dough. We enjoy this with succulent juices in sauces made from carrot mixtures. Good for 'dipping'.

4 oz rice flour
2 oz maize flour
2 oz soya flour
1 teaspoon dried parsley
$^{1}/_{4}$ teaspoon dried thyme
$^{1}/_{2}$ teaspoon dried sage
2 teaspoons Potassium baking powder
1 free range organic egg
1 tablespoon olive oil
10 fl oz water
1 tablespoon finely chopped onions

Mix up dry ingredients in a food mixer and gradually add wet ingredients.
Pour into small loaf tin and bake in hot oven for 30 mins.

Allow to cool in tin for 10 mins.
Turn out on wire tray and serve when cool.

Crispy Veg Crust

serves 4

The great benefit of potatoes is their high fibre and vitamin and mineral content.

This crust is for covering or using as a base for any of the vegetable dishes which you wish to turn into a pie. It adds a zappy topping often very attractive to children or gives a secure base to place vegetables over.

1 $^{1}/_{2}$ lb potatoes
2 tablespoons olive oil
2 oz rice flour
2 oz maize flour

Buy fairly clean looking organic newish potatoes and scrub them well. You shouldn't need to remove the skins which can be used in this dish.

Boil the potatoes until well cooked and then drain them. Mash them well and gradually add in the oil and flours. You need a fairly stiff consistency and the variety of potatoes will give different degrees of firmness. Whizz in the mixer if you have one to get all the lumps out. Spread on the base of a dish for a pie or use as a topping over any of the vegetable dishes. Cook in a medium oven for 30 mins.

Serve with seaweed scattered over the top.

Pastry

serves 4-6

This can be used to line a dish to turn one of the vegetable dishes into a tart. The flours are gluten free. Main meal casseroles could also be turned into pies.

3 oz potato flour
3 oz rice flour
3 oz non hydrogenated margarine or olive oil
Water
1 free range organic egg

Mix the two flours together and gradually crumble the fat through them until the mixture resembles breadcrumbs. This can be done in a mixer. Add egg and sufficient water (3-4 tablespoons) to form a dough mixture. Press into greased tray or pie dish. Then complete your pie or tart as required. Cook in a moderate oven for 30 mins.

Savoury Pancakes

serves 4-6

Gramflour which has long been used by Asian and Arabic communities creates a soft and pliable batter. The flour is made from a special variety of chick peas which give a rich natural source of protein and gluten free fibre.

2 cups gram flour
2 cups water
pinch of ruthmol
1 tablespoon olive oil

Mix together the flour and ruthmol in a large bowl. Make a "well" in the centre of the flour and gradually (spoon by spoon) mix in the water to create a smooth batter. Heat a small quantity of oil in a frying pan and pour in enough batter to lightly cover the base. When the mixture looks cooked and has hardened "toss" it over and cook the other side.

Serve as a base for any of the vegetable or pate recipes or as a side dish. Children love these as a pizza base.

For variations add a few slices of chilli or some herbs to give colour.

Yorkshire Pudding

serves 4

2 oz Soya Flour
2 oz Rice Flour
2 free range organic eggs
$^{1}/_{2}$ pint rice milk
2 tablespoons water
1 teaspoon olive oil

Put the flour in a large bowl and break the eggs into a well in the centre stirring into a batter mixture. Add the milk and water in a similar manner. Leave to stand, covered, for about an hour before cooking. When ready grease a serving or baking dish with the oil and pour in the batter mixture and cook in a hot oven for about 30 mins. It should puff up and be golden brown when ready.

This can be made into a scrumptious meal if vegetables are stir fried very lightly and laid in the serving dish, covered with the batter mixture and cooked as above.

Fresh Fruit Salad *serves 4*

The sweet juicy flavours of each fruit tastes delicious first thing in the morning. The best time to eat fruit is alone on an empty stomach. This prevents fermentation of other foods. Allow 20 mins before eating anything further for breakfast. Apples have plenty Vit C as have kiwi fruit who like bananas are rich in potassium. Strawberries are known for their iron content and their cleansing abilities. Grapefruit is also rich in Vit C and its soft pink colour enhances the whole dish.

2 firm green apples
2 kiwi fruit
2 small bananas
1 mango
12 strawberries
4 yellow plums
2 nectarines
1 pink grapefruit

Wash all the fruit well. Core the apples, peel the kiwi fruit, mango and grapefruit. Chop the apples, bananas, plums and nectarines and place in a bowl. Quickly cover with the segments from the grapefruit to prevent browning. Add the chopped kiwi fruit, mango, plums. nectarines and strawberries. The magnificent colours present a wholesome start to the day - enjoy.

Early Energy Muesli *several servings*

Vitamin B complex, potassium, magnesium and calcium are all present in oats and they are considered to be helpful in lowering cholesterol levels. They are a valuable source of fibre. Sunflower and pumpkin seeds are rich in zinc and their oils are very valuable. Linseeds contain large levels of the two major groups of essential fatty acids. Thus this muesli is a good basic breakfast although it can be eaten for any other meal including a light snack before bed.

3 cups organic jumbo or rolled oats
(coeliacs use millet flakes or puffed rice cereal)
3 tablespoons organic sunflower seeds
3 tablespoons organic pumpkin seeds
2 tablespoons organic pine kernels
1 tablespoon organic linseeds

optional:

2 tablespoons raisins
1 tablespoon chopped sultanas
2 tablespoons roasted buckwheat

Combine all the ingredients together and store in an air tight jar. It is easier to mix up 3 to 4 times these quantities and store them otherwise it is a constant job and early in the morning time may be at a premium.

Serve with hot or cold rice milk and as an alternative some Yofu - 'live' soya yoghurt.

SALADS

Salads are easy, quick, healthy, inexpensive, colourful and offer endless variety. One of the delights about salads is that the later you prepare the ingredients, the fresher and better they will be; just the right dish for busy people who place more importance on food for health than hours of intense advanced labour in the kitchen. Here are many ideas which you can mix and match. Again buy organic, or better still grow organic, if you can.

Beetroot Salad

serves 4

When this vegetable is eaten raw its assistance to the digestive system and especially the liver is invaluable. The raw juice is a strong blood cleanser and a potent tonic for building up the immune system.

3 good sized beetroots
1 red onion
1 tablespoon olive oil
1 tablespoon lemon juice
1 tablespoon chopped fresh coriander

Grate the beetroot and onion and mix together in a bowl. Mix together the oil and lemon juice and pour over the beetroot and onion mixture.

Place in serving dish and sprinkle the coriander over the top. Serve immediately as an accompanying salad dish

Beetroot, Cucumber & Fennel Salad

serves 4

Beetroot is sometimes known for its blood cleansing and I can remember my mother giving us the juice as a tonic. It doesn't need a dressing because its succulent juice is already moist and sweet. Cucumber is said to enhance the skin and fennel seems to help digestion.

$^{1}/_{2}$-$^{3}/_{4}$ lb beetroot
$^{1}/_{2}$ cucumber
2 small fennel bulbs
1 small red onion

Peel the beetroot and grate it. Chop the fennel and red onion into chunky slices and mix together. Place the beetroot in large bowl and with a fork stir the fennel and red onion through it. Cut the cucumber into fine straws and toss on the top. The slight staining from the beetroot juice gives this salad an unusual attractive colour toning.

This salad has to be mixed at the last minute to have the desired effect of mixed colours.

Carrot, Leek & Almond Salad

serves 4

Carrots have abundant qualities one of which is to activate and soothe the liver. For many years carrot juice has been recommended for those with liver problems. They also have strong antioxidant properties and thus could be part of a staple diet for all of us. Almonds are rich in zinc, potassium, magnesium and iron. Leeks are also rich in potassium and like their onion cousins have antibiotic qualities.

1 lb carrots
4 baby leeks (about double the size of spring onions)
3 oz almonds
small handful coriander

Wash, scrape and grate the carrots and place in large serving bowl. Thoroughly wash the leeks and chop them in small rounds and mix through the carrot to give a soft contrast. The almonds can be mixed in whole or chopped. Decorate with finely chopped coriander.

Serve immediately

Cauliflower & Broccoli Flourettes

serves 4

Another attractive salad dish portraying the ever famous broccoli which is renowned for its iron properties, helping to fight free radicals in the body and for helping with swelling joints. Radishes are rich in potassium and are said to help the activities of the liver and gall bladder.

2 heads of cauliflower
2 heads of broccoli
10 radishes

Thoroughly wash the cauliflower and broccoli and brake into small flourettes and mix together in a large serving bowl. Reserve the stalks for soup. Also wash the radishes and finely chop the leaves and scatter over the flourettes. Then chop the bulbs of the radishes into small rounds and sprinkle into the bowl. These contrasting colours give a magnificent appetising salad for all to enjoy.

Serve with herb dressing.

Coleslaw

serves 4

Cabbage and carrots give us vital nutrients full of antioxidant properties.
Carrots are said to improve our eyesight and they are also said to be recommended for respiratory and cancer difficulties. These two simple and inexpensive vegetables are definitely of great benefit to our well being. Celery is said to be anti inflammatory by clearing uric acid from the joints. Alfalfa is rich in Vit A, B,C and E, magnesium, calcium, potassium, iron, selenium and zinc. Gee -why don't we eat more of this highly nutritious food?

1 heart green cabbage
3 large carrots
4 spring onions
3 sticks celery
1 handful sprouted alfalfa

Wash the cabbage, wash and scrub the carrots, wash and string the celery and wash the spring onions. Grate them all through the attachment to your food mixer and chop any large pieces. Add some Yofu mayonnaise and transfer to a large serving dish. Decorate with alfalfa

Serve with any main dish or with baked potatoes.

French Beans, Red Lettuce & Pumpkin Seed Salad

serves 4

Pumpkin seeds renowned for their zinc properties are a lovely nutty flavour. French beans are crunchy and juicy giving bright colour to your dish when compared with the soft red lettuce.

1 large red oak leaf lettuce or radicchio
$^{1}/_{2}$ lb green french beans
2 handfuls pumpkin seeds

Thoroughly wash the lettuce to remove all grit (for some reason the red varieties seem more earthy). Use the large outside leaves to line a serving dish and tear the other leaves into smaller pieces and arrange them on the middle of the dish. Wash the green beans and arrange them in criss crosses across the lettuce. Lightly toast the pumpkin seeds and toss them on the top.

Serve with a light dressing.

Fresh & Filling Salad

serves 4

Lettuce gives us Vit C and Vit A. It is supposed to have soporific effects! Onions have strong antibiotic qualities. Potassium rich avocados contain oil which works smoothly on the digestion and their texture is soft and soothing.

2 little gem lettuces or 1 cos lettuce
1 curly lettuce
12 baby tomatoes
$^1/_2$ red onion
$^1/_2$ yellow pepper
1 avocado
3 oz cooked butter beans
3 oz cooked and shelled broad beans
1 handful fresh basil
4 spring onions
1 courgette

Wash the lettuce thoroughly and tear into bite size pieces with your hands and place in a large salad dish. Halve the baby tomatoes, thinly slice the red onion, chop the spring onions into small rounds and thinly slice the yellow pepper. Place all these ingredients in the bowl. Peel the avocado and spoon out the flesh in small rounds and add to bowl. Mix in the butterbeans and broadbeans. Cut the courgette into straws and thoroughly mix all the salad together and add the loosely chopped basil on the top.

Serve drizzled with lemon and garlic dressing.

This highly colourful and nutritious dish can be used as a main course or make smaller quantities for a side salad. If you do not have the exact ingredients improvise with what is left in the fridge.

Herbie Green Salad

serves 4-12

A large variety of lettuce leaves and herbs combined to give an attractive array of shapes, textures and flavours. If you have difficulty obtaining any of the leafy ingredients leave them out but be sure to have a selection of herbs.

1 head buttercrunch lettuce
1 head tom thumb lettuce
1 head cos lettuce
2 handfuls lambs lettuce
1 handful rocket
1 handful mizuna
1 handful fresh basil
1 handful fresh coriander
1 handful fresh chives
1 handful sprouted green lentils

Wash all the lettuces and herbs, dry them in a salad spinner and tear them into bite size strips and arrange in a large salad bowl. Sprinkle the sprouted green lentils over the top and drizzle with your chosen dressing.

Serve this when a salad is required to accompany a main dish or a portion can be served as a side salad.

Lambs Lettuce, Carrot & Sprouted Chickpea Salad

serves 4

Lambs lettuce is like watercress without the hot bite. It is a strong lettuce which keeps its shape so don't be afraid to handle it. The sprouted chickpeas give invaluable nutrition being rich in Vits A and C and calcium, magnesium and potassium and they have a very individual character.

3 handfuls lambs lettuce
1 large carrot
1 handful sprouted chickpeas
sprinkling of seaweed

Wash the lambs lettuce and scrape and grate the carrot. Arrange the lambs lettuce in a large bowl mixing the carrot through it. Toss the sprouted chickpeas over the top and sprinkle with seaweed. This is very quick and versatile and can be made in a matter of minutes.

Serve as an accompanying salad with any main dish.

Nicoise Salad *serves 4*

Most restaurants seem to feel this option has a licence to contain any ingredients available. Feel free to alter any according to what you have available. In this recipe there are eggs and salmon for protein and various lettuce and herb products to give Vits C and E. Radishes are rich in potassium and celery helps calm our nerves and it is said to have an anti-inflammatory agent which helps clear uric acid from painful joints. Red onion has antibacterial properties and the sprouts are invaluable for their vitamin, mineral and enzyme content. Avocados, of course, are very rich in essential vitamins and minerals. This is an extremely nutritious and colourful meal.

1 medium cos lettuce
1 small handful rocket
1 small lollo rossa lettuce
1 baby gem lettuce
1 small young head of celery
1 large beef tomato
$^1/_2$ handful fresh basil
1 large avocado
4 hard boiled organic free range eggs
8 oz gently steamed wild salmon
1 medium red onion
1 handful sprouted chickpeas
1 handful sprouted lentils
$^1/_2$ bunch radishes
1 handful chopped mixed garden herbs inc. chives.

Wash and tear the lettuce and place in a large salad bowl. Wash all the herbs and add them. Chop the celery into small $^1/_4$ inch pieces, thinly slice the tomato removing the core and add to bowl. Scoop the avocado out of its skin with a teaspoon, slice the eggs, remove the salmon from its skin and/ or bones, thinly slice the onion, slice the radishes and their leaves and toss all these ingredients into the bowl. Decorate the top with the sprouted chickpeas and sprouted lentils.

Serve with your chosen dressing.

Potato Salad

We obtain plentiful quantities of fibre from potatoes and they are full of Vits B and C. They are known to be helpful with circulatory and digestive disorders.

1$^1/_2$ lbs new potatoes
1 medium red onion
$^1/_2$ handful parsley
Juice of $^1/_2$ lemon
3 cloves garlic

Scrub the potatoes and cook by steaming them for about 15-20 mins. freshly dug from the garden are best and they only take a short time to cook. Check regularly because they are better when still whole and firm. Chop the garlic and parsley very finely and thinly slice the onion. Put the potatoes into a serving dish and allow to cool. Then toss in the red onion. Mix the lemon juice, garlic and parsley together and drizzle over the whole dish.

Serve with main course and other salads.

Radicchio, Chicory, Cucumber & Sesame Seed Salad

serves 4

Radicchio has a lovely tinge of deep red suggesting a good inclusion of iron in its leaves. It is said to benefit the circulatory and digestive systems and also boon our overused joints. Cucumber has always been known to have properties which are beneficial to the skin and sesame seeds are rich in zinc Vit E and essential fatty acids.

3 heads radicchio
1 head chicory
$^{1}/_{4}$ cucumber
1 handful sesame seeds

Wash the radicchio and chicory heads thoroughly. Tear them into strips and arrange in a bowl. Cut the cucumber into straws and mix through the leaves. The differing colours of white, red and green gives a lively appearance to this salad. Scatter with the sesame seeds and drizzle with your chosen dressing.

Rainbow Salad

serves 4

This extremely colourful salad is abundant with energy. Sprouted seeds give us invaluable amounts of vitamins, minerals and enzymes - they add new heights to our vital force. Be sure to use organic seeds and you will feel the goodness as you crunch them. Children really enjoy them - they sprout so quickly that each day there is something new to try. Peppers give us good sources of Vit C, betacarotene and potassium.

$^1/_2$ cup sprouted fenugreek seeds
$^1/_2$ cup sprouted chickpeas
$^1/_2$ cup sprouted alfalfa
$^1/_2$ cup sprouted green lentils
$^1/_2$ cup sprouted mung beans
$^1/_2$ cup sunflower seeds
$^1/_2$ red pepper
$^1/_2$ yellow pepper
$^1/_2$ orange pepper
$^1/_2$ green pepper
1 handful pinekernels

Slice all the peppers thinly and place them with all the sprouts in a large bowl and toss them in your hands. Add a dressing if desired (the tastes are wonderful on their own) and sprinkle the pinekernels on the top.

Eat this salad as soon as you have made it to obtain the total benefit from its freshness.

Spinach with Red Cabbage, Cauliflower & Chive Flowers

serves 4

Spinach has long been admired for its iron properties and in its raw state is helpful for tiredness or anaemic tendencies. Similarly the benefits of cabbage in its raw state are numerous and its high chlorophyll content is advantageous for digestion, tiredness, circulation and fighting cancer. Chive flowers not only give fabulous colour but as members of the onion family have antibiotic qualities. They are slightly hot and should be pulled apart when eaten to spread their effect.

1 lb raw young spinach
$^1/_2$ medium red cabbage
4 oz cauliflower florets
8 chive flowers

Thoroughly wash the spinach and arrange on a large serving dish. Grate the red cabbage and pile on top leaving the edges clear. Wash the cauliflower florets and stack on top again and finally wash the chive flowers and arrange them on the top.

This gives a vivid contrasting colour to a very nutritious salad. Add dressing of your choice - if you wish.

Tomato & Sprouted Alfalfa *serves 4*

Tomatoes are said to improve our circulatory, respiratory and digestive systems. The Mediterranean countries seem to have heeded this information for many years but they are probably most beneficial when raw. This dish is quick and simple to prepare and looks most appetising with its blend of colours.

- $1^1/_2$ lbs tomatoes
- 1 handful sprouted alfalfa
- 1 tablespoon chopped basil

Slice the tomatoes finely with a sharp knife and place them on a serving plate. Sprinkle with the chopped basil and cover with the sprouted alfalfa.

This is suitable either as an accompanying salad to a main dish or to eat for lunch with rice.

Watercress, Red Onion & Sunflower Seeds Salad

serves 4

Watercress is rich in Vits A and C and Potassium Its slightly hot flavour gives extra character to a very useful food which has antibiotic qualities. Its iodine properties are helpful in the treatment of underactive thyroids.
Sunflower seeds are overflowing with mineral wealth and essential oil and lend a crisp nutty character to your salad. The vibrant red and green colours make this a most attractive dish.

1 large bunch watercress
1 large red onion
2 oz sunflower seeds

Thoroughly wash the watercress several times and dry in a salad spinner. Finely slice the onions. Slightly toast the sunflower seeds. In a large bowl toss the watercress lightly, mixing the onion rings through it and scatter the sunflower seeds on the top. Serve with any main dish immediately as it is or drizzle with your favourite dressing.

SAUCES & DRESSINGS

You can transform the simplest of recipes into a memorable meal with one of these sauces or dressings. Forget the heavy white sauces made from butter, flour and milk. Herbs, spices and healthy ingredients can give zest to each and every meal that will have your family and guests eager to learn your cooking skills.

Aubergine Dressing

Tahini is made from roasted sesame seeds which have good zinc properties and its oily texture lends itself to dressings. The aubergine gives this dressing a good colour and texture.

$^{1}/_{2}$ medium aubergine
2 tablespoons tahini
2 cloves garlic
1 handful fresh coriander
$^{1}/_{4}$ pt rice milk
1 teaspoon dried cumin powder

Chop the aubergine well and then whiz all ingredients in the liquidiser except for the rice milk. Drizzle this in slowly until a 'dressing' consistency is reached. Serve with salads or vegetables.

Broadbean Sauce

This delicious silky green sauce is a pleasant accompaniment to fish - either hot or cold. Not only does it add variety to the colour of grilled fish but the unusual flavour keeps your guests guessing. It has a different pea style flavour.

1 lb broadbeans
$^1/_2$ cup rice milk
dash of pepper
add grated horseradish to give a little nip (1teaspoon raw)
2 teaspoons lime juice

Blanch the broadbeans in boiling water for a couple of minutes. Rinse in cold water and shell them. Put the green soft beans into the rice milk and simmer for a few minutes and then liquidise them adding a little pepper, horseradish and the lime juice.

Delicious with fish *or* if you wish to use this sauce as a dip for crudeties then just cut back on the amount of liquid used to keep it a little thicker.

Coconut Curry Sauce

1 medium onion
4 cloves garlic
1 inch fresh ginger
1 large red pepper
1 tablespoon paprika
$^1/_2$ teaspoon powdered turmeric
$^1/_4$ teaspoon chilli powder
2 tablespoons olive oil
1 $^1/_2$ pints vegetable stock
1 stick fresh lemongrass (can use dried - 3-4 tablespoons)
1 inch fresh galangal (can use dried - 2 tablespoons)
8 oz creamed coconut or tinned coconut

Dried lemon grass and dried galangal will need to be soaked for 30 mins before use. Otherwise slice the fresh lemon grass and chop the fresh galangal, finely chop the onions and garlic, peel and chop the ginger, chop the pepper and blend all these in the liquidiser with the paprika, turmeric and chilli powders. Heat oil in a pan and tip the mixture from the liquidiser into it and fry for at least 10 mins. Add the stock and bring to the boil stirring all the time. Leave to simmer for 20-30 mins. Then strain through a sieve. Return to the pan and gradually stir in the coconut milk.

It is a vibrant colour and should be sauce consistency. If you need it thicker add more coconut milk but this will reduce the heat of the sauce. If you need it thinner then add more stock.

The sauce can be made well in advance and kept in the fridge. Use it when you need glamour in the form of colour or for an unusual flavour with fish or pulse dishes. It is always a success with guests!

Gazpacho Dressing

This is a deliciously appetising dressing which enhances the look and flavour of different lettuces. The proportions are variable according to what you have available. Remember the cucumber is mostly liquid and probably shouldn't be increased.

1 clove garlic
$^{1}/_{2}$ fresh green chilli
$^{1}/_{2}$ small cucumber
$^{1}/_{2}$ red pepper
3 spring onions
$^{1}/_{4}$ pt olive oil
1 tablespoon apple cider vinegar
1 tablespoon lemon juice
1 tablespoon fresh oregano or basil
2 pinches black pepper

Whiz all the ingredients in the liquidiser and keep in the fridge. Shake well and drizzle over salad, vegetables or rice with a spoon.

Harissa

Use for flavouring soups, casseroles or sauces. Keep in fridge. This is a large amount (130g or more) to save making it too often.

$^1/_2$ pint olive oil
1-2 bulbs of garlic
3 oz toasted coriander seeds or ground coriander powder
$1^1/_2$ oz toasted cumin seeds or ground cumin powder
Large (3 inch) slice peeled fresh root ginger
3 fresh red chillies
1 teaspoon paprika
Juice of 1 lemon

Blend all these ingredients first slowly and gradually faster in the liquidiser until a smooth paste is formed. It gives a hot tasty condiment to enhance the flavour of many dishes. It is used widely in Moroccan cuisine and so your dishes can take on descriptions from this country!

Lemon & Garlic Dressing

Lemons are rich in Vit C and help to stimulate the immune system thus fighting infections. The antibacterial properties of garlic are well known and it seems to act as an anticoagulant thus helpful for lowering blood pressure and cholesterol levels.

Juice of $^1/_2$ - 1 lemon
4 cloves garlic
3 tablespoons olive oil
3 tablespoons flaxseed oil
$^1/_2$ teaspoon apple juice concentrate

Crush the garlic cloves and mix with the olive and flaxseed oil and stir in the syrup. Gradually add the lemon juice according to both taste and desired consistency. Add a little water to thin it if needed. It is ideal to make large quantities and keep this in the fridge.

Serve drizzled onto any salad or over steamed vegetables.

Mayonnaise

1 cup cashew nuts
Juice of $^{1}/_{2}$ lemon
2 cloves garlic
Equal quantities of olive oil and nut seed oil
(about 3 tablespoons of each)
Handful fresh basil

Pour 2 tablespoons of olive oil and nut oil into a liquidiser and gradually add the cashew nuts. This will become fairly thick - then thin it down gradually adding lemon juice. To thicken add the remainder of the oils. When the correct consistency is reached add garlic and basil. Keep in fridge and use with salads, fish and vegetables.

Pesto

Basil is considered to be calming for the nervous system and a natural tranquilliser. This can be used as a dip, thick sauce or spread. It is delicious added to casseroles and soups and its strong basil flavour gives a Mediterranean flair to a dish. It is an excellent accompaniment to fish and vegetable or rice dishes. It has a beautiful colour which can enhance any dish. Large quantities can be made and kept in the fridge or freezer. This recipe makes about 120-150g.

1 cup pine kernels
1 handful fresh basil
1 tablespoon olive oil
pinch of pepper

Mix together in liquidiser.
If you want a more liquid sauce then add water.

Serve with vegetables or fish.

Quick Red Sauce

serves 4

This sauce can be used to enhance fish dishes or to drizzle over salads. Do not use if you are cutting out or down on tomatoes as these are cooked.

6 oz sundried tomatoes - soaked in advance for about an hour
2 cupfuls of shelled raw peas
1 onion

Sweat the onion in a little water. Once the tomatoes have been soaked put them in a pan with the peas and add enough water to cover them. Cook gently for about 10 mins. When all are soft liquidise and add more water if too thick. Cook slightly and then either pour over fish or drizzle over a fresh salad.

Salsa

serves 8-10

This is so useful and you can change it to suit your needs. Use any herbs you have handy and alter the amounts of oil according to how thick or runny you need it for the particular dish you have chosen to accompany.

Basil calms the nervous system, coriander aids digestion, chives like their cousins garlic and onion have antioxidant qualities and parsley rich in Vit A and C as well as iron, calcium and potassium has diuretic qualities and it clears any breath odour.

2 handfuls fresh coriander
2 handfuls fresh parsley
1 handful fresh chives
3 handfuls fresh basil
4 garlic cloves
4 tablespoons virgin olive oil

Wash the herbs and put them all in the liquidiser with half the olive oil and whiz for a couple of minutes at high speed. Turn the speed down and drizzle in the rest of the oil as needed for a fairly smooth consistency.

Serve with fish. burgers or salads.

Spicy Dressing

about 20-30 servings

Delicious with either hot or cold dishes. Cayenne can improve circulation and bring warmth to cold extremities and troubled joints. Garlic is well known for its anti bacterial qualities. Coriander, widely used in the Far East, is enjoyed for its assistance in digestion and turmeric helps elimination through sweating. Cinnamon is an antiseptic.

4 cloves garlic
1 tablespoon coriander powder
1 tablespoon cumin powder
2 tablespoon cayenne
1 tablespoon turmeric
1 cinnamon stick
$^1/_2$ pint olive oil

Heat the oil. Meanwhile crush the garlic cloves and add all the ingredients to the oil. Cook for about 10 mins but do not allow to boil. Leave to stand in a warm place for a day. Remove the cinnamon stick. Taste. Can be served hot or cold.

Serve with fish, roasts, burgers and all vegetable or salad dishes.

Tangy Nut Dressing

An exotic flavour - difficult for others to decipher the ingredients! Very useful to enhance vegetable and salad dishes. Almonds and cashews have high protein contents so this can enrich a convalescent's diet

2 oz shelled cashews
2 oz shelled almonds
2 garlic cloves
1 small onion
2 tablespoons olive or nut oil
1 teaspoon apple juice concentrate (optional)
Juice of 1 lime
$^1/_2$ teaspoon chilli powder
$^1/_2$ pint water

Finely chop the onion and garlic and sauté in the oil for about 3 mins. Meanwhile put the nuts into a liquidiser on fast. Add the water and nuts to the onions and garlic and add the chilli powder and apple juice concentrate. Stir this mixture as it thickens and comes to the boil. Continue cooking for another 10 or so minutes and it will become creamy. Remove from the heat and leave to cool slightly before stirring in the lime juice. Add this slowly, tasting as you go and then you can adjust the taste to suit. If you want the dressing to be thicker then use less water.

Tomato, Lime & Chive Salsa

serves 4

A salsa is a useful accompaniment to any dish because it adds a delicate moist sauce which is usually very light. The pungent flavour of the lime brings up the distinctiveness of the tomatoes and chives and enhances fish, nut and vegetable dishes.

Juice and zest of 1 lime
$^1/_2$ lb firm tomatoes
Handful of garden chives
1 tablespoon olive oil or nut oil

Scoop out the seeds from the tomatoes and reserve for another dish.

Mix all ingredients vigorously in the liquidiser reserving some of the lime juice in case it becomes too liquid. Serve immediately with your chosen dish.

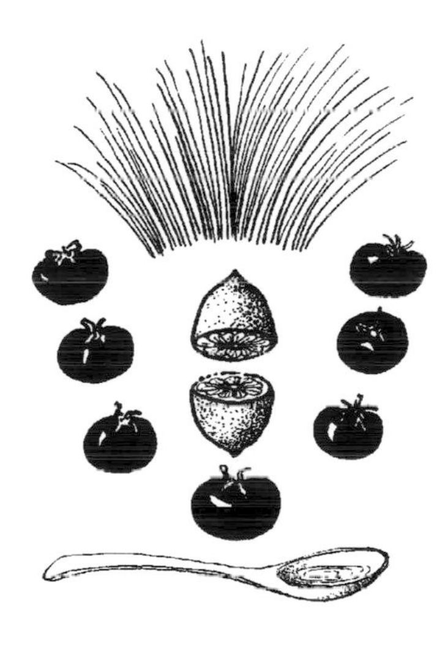

Yofu Mayonnaise

serves 4

To enliven some salads and vegetable dishes this mayonnaise is extremely useful. The Yofu soya yoghurt is "live" and so helpful for our internal bacteria. Tahini is made from sesame seeds and is rich in calcium.

8 oz Yofu
2 tablespoons tahini
Juice of 1 small lemon
1 handful fresh chives

Finely chop the chives and keep aside. Mix all the other ingredients in a bowl and finally stir in the chives. If you need a runny consistency then add water if you need it thick limit the amount of lemon juice.

Serve with any main dish, salad or vegetables.

STARTERS, SOUPS & SNACKS

A freshly prepared starter at the beginning of a meal knocks the stuffing out of cloying sweets and puddings which can weigh you down when you have already eaten enough. These versatile recipes can be adapted to whet your appetite as an accompaniment to Summer evening aperitifs under a clear sky or boost your energy and renew your vigour with a robust Winter warmer at lunch time on a cold, February afternoon.

Soups can also be used for a main dish when time is at a premium but nutrition is the optimum aim.

Asparagus Mousse

serves 4

Asparagus is said to benefit the liver and kidneys. Choose small sized asparagus for this dish as the larger ones tend to become rather 'woody'.

1 bundle asparagus
3 tablespoons Yofu or 2 Soya Cream
$^1/_4$ teaspoon paprika

Cut away about 3 inches from the bottom of the asparagus and wash thoroughly. Steam the asparagus for 6-8 mins. Reserve the water for a soup. Reserve 4 small tips for decoration. Mix the asparagus with the Yofu or soya cream in a liquidiser until soft and creamy. Add some of the water if it is too stiff.

Spoon into individual serving dishes or place on a bed of salad leaves. Decorate with the reserved tips and sprinkle with the paprika. Alternatively this mousse can be used as a dip for crudities or a paté and served with rice cakes.

Aubergine Paté *serves 4-6*

This is a highly colourful pate which can be served as a snack or starter.

2 large aubergines
4 cloves garlic
Juice of 1 lemon
3 tablespoons tahini
4 sprigs of coriander leaves

Chop the aubergines into small pieces and put them into a food processor with the garlic. Add half the lemon juice and tahini and then whiz altogether. Gradually add the rest of the lemon juice and tahini according to the consistency you require. Turn into attractive serving dish and decorate with the coriander leaves.

Serve with rice cakes or oatcakes.

Avocado Paté

serves 4

Potassium rich avocado is a complete food and therefore very nutritious for everyone. It is high in the anti oxidants vitamins A, C and E and is known for its facility for producing smooth skin which is supple.
Enjoy!

1 ripe avocado
3 spring onions
1 tablespoon Yofu 'live' soya yoghurt
1 garlic clove
shaking of paprika

Peel and stone the avocado, chop the spring onions and garlic clove very finely and mix thoroughly in a bowl with the Yofu. Put in serving dish and sprinkle with a little paprika.

Serve with rice cakes as a snack or starter. Decorate with a few salad leaves.

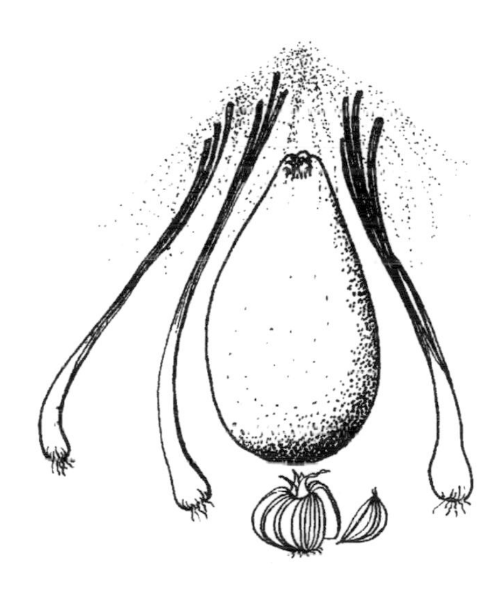

Avocado Surprise *a delicious starter for 4*

This no cholesterol fruit is often used as a vegetable and it has remarkable nutritional properties. It is stacked with essential vitamins and minerals including Vit E hence it is helpful for keeping skin youthful. It is free of sodium and rich in magnesium, calcium and potassium.

2 Ripe avocados
Salad leaves
'Surprise filling'
Mayonnaise or Dressing
Pinch of Paprika

Line a small dish with washed salad leaves.
Halve and stone and peel the avocado.
Mix the 'surprise' filling.
Fill the cavity in the avocado and turn upsidedown on the salad leaves
Cover with home made mayonnaise or dressing.
Sprinkle with the paprika.

For 'surprise filling' see other recipes e.g. hummus, pesto, salsa or mayonnaise.

Beetroot Soup

serves 4

This sweet root vegetable has long been considered a competent cleanser for the entire digestive system. This soup tastes extremely sweet and its rich velvet colour lends value to a most attractive dish.

4 large beetroot
2 medium apples and or onions
soya cream

Peel beetroot and apples if used and cut into small pieces.
Cut onion into same size pieces.
Cover with water and simmer until soft.
Liquidize until consistency is smooth.
Return to pan and bring back to nearly boiling.

Serve with dash of soya cream and rice cakes.

Buckwheat & Roots Soup

serves 4-6

Buckwheat is said to be good for the circulatory system because of its rutin content. Rutin is helpful with high blood pressure. The Polish peasants used it regularly where it was a cheap standby.

1 tablespoon olive oil
1 lb carrots
$^1/_2$ lb parsnips
$^1/_4$ teaspoon cumin powder
$^1/_2$ cup fresh coriander
1 cup cooked buckwheat
2 onions
2-3 pts water

Make this recipe to suit your size of servings

Fry onion in oil and then add chopped carrots and parsnips (swede or turnip can be used instead).
Add water and cooked buckwheat.
Simmer for half to one hour or put in slow oven for an hour.
Liquidise and add the chopped coriander saving a little to sprinkle on top of each serving.

Butterbean & Carrot Soup

serves 4-8

Butterbeans are an adaptable pulse and their protein and fibre content are invaluable. They are very tasty and their pliable texture gives a good creamy effect when liquidized in a soup.

8 oz butterbeans (soaked and cooked)
1 lb carrots
1 teaspoon ground ginger
2 cloves garlic
1 large onion
3 pts or more of water
sprinkling of dried seaweed for each serving

Chop carrots and put in pan, adding ginger, chopped garlic cloves, chopped onion and butterbeans and enough water to cover everything well. Cook for about an hour and then liquidise to a smooth creamy consistency.
Serve with a sprinkling of fine seaweed.

Carrot Soup with a Kick *serves 4-6*

Carrots have so many nutritious properties. They have high antioxidant content i.e. Vits A, C and E. and their juice is beneficial for maintaining a healthy liver. This simple soup therefore is not only a splendid food but also an easy standby for all the family. Its bright appearance makes it very appetising.

3 lbs. organic carrots
2 medium onions
$^{1}/_{3}$ fresh red pepper
vegetable stock to cover (about 2 pints)
handful of fresh chives

Simmer carrots, onions and pepper in stock until soft.
Liquidise to a smooth soup.
Chop chives very finely.
Serve with a sprinkling of chopped chives on top.

Courgette & Fennel Soup *serves 4*

Fennel is well known for its assistance with digestion and it blends beautifully with the highly coloured courgette to give a rich green appetising soup.

1 medium onion
2 cloves garlic
1 dessertspoon olive oil
1 $^{1}/_{2}$ lbs courgettes
1 $^{1}/_{2}$ pts veg stock
1 teaspoon fennel seeds
250 ml soya cream - optional

Sauté the chopped onion and garlic in the oil for 5 mins. Add the well chopped courgettes and the fennel seeds. Cook for further 5 mins. Add the stock, bring to the boil and simmer for $^{1}/_{2}$ hour. Liquidise until smooth. Add a swirl of cream in the centre of each serving bowl if desired.

Serve with corn bread.

Fanned Avocado

serves 4

This attractive pear has wonderful properties for keeping the skin supple and young. It is rich in potassium and magnesium - two minerals which are essential for good health and contains good sources of antioxidant vitamins A,C and E. It has good quantities of vitamin K and folic acid both of which are essential for healthy blood thus the pear's help for improving circulation has been known for many years. It is very easy to digest and is a welcome food for convalescents. It has low carbohydrate content and no cholesterol.

2 ripe Avocados
1 oz Toasted Pine Kernels
(spread on baking tray and place in cool oven until slightly browned - approx 8 mins.)

Dressing

Juice of half a lemon
1 tablespoon flax seed oil
$^{1}/_{2}$ tablespoon olive oil
1 teaspoon rice syrup
1 tablespoon Yofu (live tofu yoghurt)

Halve and stone the avocado. Lay it flat on a plate, cut at an angle and spread into a fan shape.

Mix all the dressing ingredients together and drizzle over the top of the avocado.

Sprinkle with the toasted pine kernels.

Herbie Fish Soup

serves 4

Like most soups this can be used either as a starter or a main course chowder. It is light and tasty. Fish is said to be good food for the brain and the oil it contains is an essential fatty acid which the body needs to emulsify the skin, maintain strong healthy nails, fight infections, and among other things keep the joints lubricated.

1 onion
1 head of garlic
10 oz fresh white fish (haddock or cod are good)
1 oz fresh basil
handful of fresh coriander
1 tablespoon fresh parsley
1 tablespoon fresh tarragon
1 pint fish stock
1 dessertspoon olive oil

Sauté onions and garlic in oil and add fish stock.
Cook for about 20 mins.

Pull the fish into small pieces and cook in the soup for about 3 mins until soft then take it out and keep warm.

Chop all the herbs and add to soup and blend. Cook a further 5 mins.

Keep a little parsley to sprinkle on top of soup.

Add the reserved cooked fish and serve.

Hummus

serves several

This is a Middle Eastern dish and is very versatile. It can either be used for a starter or a spread for rice cakes or to top corn bread. It can be kept in the fridge and used for snacks and lunches. You can play around with the texture - keeping it more formed for spreading or more liquified if it is going to be tipped over salad leaves.

4 oz dried chickpeas
juice of one lemon
2 cloves of garlic
2 tablespoons tahini
sprinkling of paprika
1 tablespoon of olive oil
1 tablespoon flaxseed oil
little water
pinch of ruthmol

Wash and soak the chickpeas overnight.

Drain and put in pan of fresh water , bring to boil and cook for about $^{1}/_{2}$ - 1 hour or until soft.

Put in a blender with some water to make a thick paste. Add ruthmol.

Add the lemon, tahini and garlic and blend again.

Sprinkle with paprika

Serve with rice cakes as a starter or snack
or
serve on bed of salad leaves.

Mangetout Soup

serves 4

This variety of peas enables us to eat the whole thing, pods and all. They are plentiful in Vits A, C and E. Mint has long been considered a herb which has a calming effect on the digestive tract.

1 medium onion
1 $^1/_2$ lbs mangetout
1 dessertspoon olive oil
$^1/_2$ handful fresh mint
1 large potato
water

Finely chop the onion and lightly sauté in the oil for 5 mins. Scrub the potato, chop into small pieces and add. Cook for a further 5 mins. Top and tail the mangetout and add them to the pan and cover with water. Bring to the boil and leave to simmer for $^1/_2$ hour or until the vegetables are soft. Pour the mixture into a mixer and liquidise until smooth and return to the pan adding more water depending on the consistency you require. Chop the mint finely and sprinkle on the top of each serving.

Serve with rice or oatcakes.

Mint Paté

serves 4-6

Mint traditionally has a calming effect on the digestive tract and its strong distinctive flavour gives a very original satisfying pate.

8 oz cooked black eyed or haricot beans (see Pulses)
1 small onion
2 cloves garlic
1 handful fresh mint

Whiz all the ingredients in a liquidiser until a smooth paste is formed. Gradually add water if it is too stiff.

Serve with rice cakes or rice bread or on a bed of salad leaves.

Parsnip & Fennel Soup *serves 4*

Fennel has for years been said to aid the digestive system and its distinctive flavour blends beautifully with the strong aromatic taste of parsnips thus producing a tasty soup.

1 $^1/_2$ lbs parsnips
2 whole fennel bulbs
Approx 2 pints veg stock
pinch seaweed

Cook the scraped, chopped parsnips and trimmed and chopped fennel in $^1/_2$ pt of stock. When soft liquidise on low number so some chunky pieces are left and it is not a smooth paste. Add the rest of the stock according to how thick or thin you require the soup to be. Return to pan to warm through.

Serve with a pinch of seaweed scattered over the top of each bowl and rice cakes.

Pumpkin Soup

serves 4-6

Actually this is almost a casserole it is so substantial. Pumpkins are rich in beta carotene and thus help us to build the immunity to fight off unwanted germs. Their orange flesh is said to be helpful in defending our systems against respiratory problems, cancers and heart disease.

2 lbs pumpkin
1 teaspoon olive oil
2 cloves garlic
3 oz yellow split peas
1 medium red onion
2 pts veg stock
3 inches raw ginger
Teaspoon of seaweed

Remove the seeds from the pumpkin and cut it into a few large pieces and bake it covered in a medium oven for half an hour. Meanwhile finely chop the garlic and onion and sauté in the olive oil for 5 mins. Add the split peas and veg stock and bring to the boil. Remove the pumpkin from the oven and scoop the flesh into the stock. Simmer for 45 mins. Liquidise with a hand mixer.

Sprinkle with seaweed and serve with corn bread. For maximum gourmet display this can be served inside a pumpkin case - excellent for children at Halloween!

Rich Green Paté

serves 4-6

This is an extremely tasty paté that can be used as a snack at any time. Full of mineral wealth and anti bacterial qualities it helps you feel fresh and full of life.

1 ripe avocado
2 cloves garlic
2 tablespoons Yofu
4 spring onions
Juice of $^{1}/_{2}$ lemon

Peel and stone the avocado and squash with a fork. Finely chop the garlic and spring onions using the green parts as well. Mix all ingredients together and pour into serving bowl.

Serve with rice cakes, oat cakes or add water to make it runnier and use as a dressing for salads.

Salmon Sorbet

serves 4

Salmon is an oily fish thus bearing properties of fats essential for our well being. Yofu is a live soya (non genetically modified) product which can be used for any mousses or pastes. This sorbet is a light dish and is probably best used as a starter.

8 oz cooked salmon
4 tablespoons Yofu
1 tablespoon horseradish
A squeeze of lemon juice
pinch of pepper

Flake the salmon and mix it in a liquidiser with the Yofu and add the other ingredients and mix again. Spoon into a bowl and freeze until ready to serve.

Remove from freezer and allow to thaw for about half an hour. Serve on a bed of mixed salad leaves and sprinkle the top with paprika.

Tomato Marrons

serves 4

This is an easy stand by for a starter and provides lots of colour. Tomatoes are considered to be a tremendous anti-oxidant and therefore are a useful ingredient as the Italians and Mexicans show us. The blend of tomatoes and chestnuts gives an unusual sweet and savoury flavour which is gentle at the beginning of a meal.

4 beef tomatoes
1 large onion
8 oz cooked chestnuts
4 fresh baby asparagus
small mixture of salad leaves

Cut top off beef tomatoes and reserve.
Remove centre from tomatoes.

Sauté onion and add about half of the centres from the tomatoes.

Chop up the cooked chestnuts and add to onion and tomato and heat for 10 mins.

Remove and liquidise or stir vigorously to obtain smooth paste. Place this paste in the empty tomato cavities and put lid on top.

Serve either hot or cold on a bed of lettuce leaves.

Put one piece of asparagus through centre of tomato to give chimney effect.

Yummy Yam Soup

serves 4

Yams are a regular vegetable in the East. They are said to have hormonal qualities which benefit middle aged and upwards citizens. They have a particularly orange coloured look and a fairly sweet flavour thus giving an unusual addition to the soup menus.

1 lb yams or sweet potatoes
1 large onion
2 cloves garlic
1/2 lb carrots
1 1/2 pts vegetable stock
2 tablespoons olive oil
1/2 teaspoon dried seaweed

Peel the yams and chop them. Cover with water. Bring them to the boil and simmer for about 20 mins until soft and then drain them and chop them into 2 inch pieces. Heat the oil and sauté the chopped onion and garlic. Add the scraped and chopped carrots and cook for about 5 mins. Then add the chopped yams and half of the stock. Cook for a further 5 mins and then puree everything in the liquidiser. Return to the pan and add the remaining stock. Reheat and season if necessary with ruthmol but as the taste should be sweet don't ruin it. Sprinkle a little seaweed on each portion for decoration.

Serve the soup with rice cakes.

As an alternative - this same mixture could be made into a "mash" by limiting the amount of stock added and then when the mixture is liquidised it will create a thicker compact blend which could be served with main meals or with steamed vegetables piled on top.

MAIN COURSES

Here are some recipes that will restore your faith in the benefit of a hearty main course and tempt your family back for regular meals.

By now you have already dispensed with the fatty sauces and bought processed meals. From California to Timbuktu, Iceland to Italy, eating a nutritious, daily meal can be a delight as well as a course of life giving energy. Whilst poor communities strive to achieve the wherewithal to achieve one nourishing meal a day, richer nations can squander money on unsatisfying fast foods and non-nourishing snacks.

Many of the recipes and food combinations in this book will cause you to re-think your way of eating. Millet is not just for budgerigars and pulses are aptly named for their heart and blood benefits. Rice is a healthy food eaten the world over and generations of expertise have created a host of appetising recipes.

Butterbean & Lentil Bake *serves 6-8*

This dish is a wonderful winter warmer. The butterbeans and lentils are both good sources of protein and blended together in this dish they have a lovely nutty flavour. Lentils contain high levels of potassium, iron and zinc and are easy on the digestion.

6 oz Butterbeans
6 oz Red lentils
8-10 oz Potatoes
2 medium onions
Handful fresh chopped rosemary
1 tablespoon olive oil
2 pts veg stock

Soak the butterbeans overnight.
Cook rapidly in fresh water until tender 1-$1^1/_2$ hours
In separate pan cover lentils with veg stock and cook until soft - about 30 mins. Add more water if necessary.
(if they are also soaked it reduces their cooking time).
As they cook they will form a thick sauce.

Fry onion in olive oil.
Add lentil sauce.
Place butter beans in casserole dish and pour sauce over top.
Peel and scrape potatoes and slice in thin strips and place over the top of butterbean and lentil mixture.
Drizzle with olive oil or paint onto potatoes.
Cook in hot oven for about half an hour or until browned.

Serve with brown rice to make a complete protein and salad or steamed veg.

Chestnut & Sprout Casserole

serves 4

This dish is very quick to prepare and the chestnuts give it a Christmas flavour. The taste is even better if made in advance and kept for the next day as the juices blend together and give a succulent experience of richness.

1 onion
1 lb sprouts
12 oz chestnuts (cooked)
2 cloves garlic
arrowroot for thickening
$^1/_2$ to $^3/_4$ pt vegetable stock
olive oil

Fry the garlic and onion very lightly in the olive oil.
Add the washed and prepared sprouts, some halved.
Add the chestnuts and cook for 5 mins.
Add small quantity of stock to give casserole consistency - if liquid is too thin sprinkle with arrowroot and stir well, adding more stock if necessary.

This is delicious with a carrot mash

Chickpea & Sweet Potato Patties

serves 4

This dish is quick to make and very satisfying. The chickpeas bring plant protein to the fore and when served with rice or millet give a complete protein. Remember to soak the chickpeas in water overnight - they will increase in size and are then ready to be boiled. The sweet potatoes are good sources of potassium, calcium, carotenes and Vit C. The firmer and darker they are the sweeter they seem to taste.

> $^1/_2$ lb chickpeas
> $^1/_2$ lb sweet potatoes
> Juice from 1 apple
> 2 tablespoons chopped fresh parsley

Soak the chickpeas overnight and cook according to guidelines in Pulses information.
Cover the potatoes with water and cook until soft.
Mash the sweet potatoes and chickpeas together and mix thoroughly. Add the apple juice and the chopped parsley.
Form into 8 round patties and then place on greased ovenproof dish and cook in moderate oven for approx 15 mins.

Serve with mixed vegetables, rice and salad.

Courgette & Chickpea Savoury Cakes

serves 4

Chickpeas are used as a staple part of diet in the Middle East. Remember to soak and cook them well before adding to this dish. It is fairly difficult to determine the origins of this dish and children seem to love it. When served with brown rice the complete protein is then provided as the essential amino acids are then present.

- 1 tablespoon olive oil
- 1 medium onion
- 4 cloves garlic
- 2 tablespoons fresh coriander
- 2 teaspoons dried cumin powder
- 4 courgettes
- 6 oz chickpeas (ready soaked and cooked)
- 1 egg
- 2 tablespoons gram flour

Fry onions and garlic in oil stirring in spices.
Add the very finely chopped or grated courgettes and cook for about 5 mins.
Add the cooked chickpeas, then blend altogether with an egg.
Roll in gram flour and shape into small cakes.
Bake in oven for 15 mins or until slightly browned.

Serve with a salad and shortgrain brown rice.

Courgettes with Carrot, Ginger & Almond Stuffing *serves 4-6*

This can be prepared well in advance. It looks particularly colourful and tastes terrific with the clever blend of flavours. The ginger is particularly helpful with digestion and so it is a great appetiser for a dinner party. The garlic and onions are both antibacterial and are known to act as anticoagulants - lowering both blood pressure and cholesterol levels.

2 onions
1 tablespoon olive oil
4 small courgettes
2 cloves of garlic
2 large carrots
1 inch of fresh ginger - grated
shake of black pepper
1 oz of chopped up almonds

Fry onion and garlic in oil.
Halve courgettes lengthways and scoop out centres.
Chop up centres and add to onion and garlic.
Dice or grate carrot and add, also add ginger.
Cook for about 10 mins in a pan.

Remove from heat and add almonds and pepper.
Put courgette skins into casserole dish and fill with mixture.

Cover and cook in oven until tender - about 20 -30 mins

Egg & Nut Kedgeree *serves 4*

Full of nourishing proteins this dish offers a light supper dish or a main course dinner. It is best prepared just before eating and not left to keep warm when it might deteriorate. Free range organic eggs, free from factory farming chemicals give first class protein, zinc and Vits B. Rice is a good cleanser for the gastro intestinal tract. The avocado too is rich in many vitamins and minerals as are the nuts and so this delicate dish might be considered excellent for recuperation.

2 cups cooked brown rice
4 hard boiled free range organic eggs - chopped
1 avocado - chopped
1 oz hazelnuts - chopped
1 oz brazil nuts - chopped
2 tablespoons well chopped onion
1 dessertspoon olive oil
1 teaspoon cumin powder
1 teaspoon coriander powder
1 small carton soya cream (usually 250ml)
$^1/_4$ pt rice milk
pinch of dried seaweed

Sauté the onion in the olive oil until soft and add the avocado - cook for 2-3 mins.
Add the seasonings, cream and enough milk to give a thick consistency and bring to simmering.
Remove from heat and bind in the rice, eggs and nuts.
Return to heat and bring back to simmer for about 5-10 mins.
Try not to stir too much as the pieces will break up.
Empty onto serving dish and sprinkle with dried seaweed.

This is a colourful dish and can be served alone or with a salad

Fish Cake Feast

serves 4

Fish gives us a good source of protein and essential fatty acids. These fish cakes are quick to make and can be prepared ahead of time and kept in the fridge until you are ready to cook them. Among parsley's qualities are its ability to help eliminate uric acid from the system and its diuretic action.

1 lb haddock, cod or hake
1 lb potatoes
2 oz parsley
2 tablespoons gram flour
1 egg

Steam the fish for ten minutes until flaky. Boil the potatoes gently until soft. Finely chop the parsley. Mash the potatoes and mix with the fish adding the chopped parsley. Mix together well adding any of the steaming water if needed. Shape into 8 rounds and roll in gram flour, then drop into beaten egg and roll in gram flour again to coat and put in fridge for at least half an hour.

Bake in medium over for 20-30 mins

Serve with fresh leafy salad and herb salsa

Fish Kedgeree

serves 4

This is a wonderful dish for using up left overs or else buy the ingredients especially. Any fish will do (salmon for colour) but if making it from scratch haddock is very tasty. In years gone by kedgeree was served for breakfast when rich food was eaten for all meals - its a good standby evening meal with strong protein properties and very quick to make.

10 oz haddock
pinch white pepper
1 cup cooked short grain brown rice
$^1/_2$ pt rice milk
1 dessertspoon arrowroot or cornflour
2 tablespoons soya cream or coconut milk
handful fresh parsley

Simmer the fish in a little rice milk for 4 mins and then drain and pull the fish into flaked pieces about the size of a walnut. Meanwhile make a thick white sauce by warming the milk and separately making a paste with the cornflour or arrowroot and a little water and gradually combining the two. Add any milk left over from the fish. Combine the sauce with the rice. Add the soya cream or coconut milk and cook together for 3-4 mins until hot. Turn into serving dish and decorate with chopped fresh parsley.

Serve either with a salad or steamed green vegetables.

Fricassee of Halibut

serves 4

The oil in fish is considered beneficial to the heart and helps with circulatory problems. I have used halibut here as it is a very chewy fish and it doesn't brake up when cooked but other fish such as hake, cod and salmon would also be suitable.

1 $^1/_2$ lbs halibut (boned and skinned)
8 oz soya cream
1 tablespoon olive oil
Grated rind of 2 limes
Juice of 2 limes
$^1/_4$ teaspoon cayenne pepper

1 courgette
1 carrot
Handful french beans
6 small yellow squash

Steam the vegetables until they are 'al dente' (about 4 mins) and keep warm.
Pull or cut the fish into small 1 inch pieces so that they are not uniformed and season with the cayenne. Heat the oil and toss the fish in it - remove fish and keep it warm in the serving dish.
Add the ginger, soya cream and rind and juice of the limes in the same pan and cook until this gives a thick sauce consistency. Pour the sauce over the fish and arrange the vegetables over the top. This can also be done on individual plates.

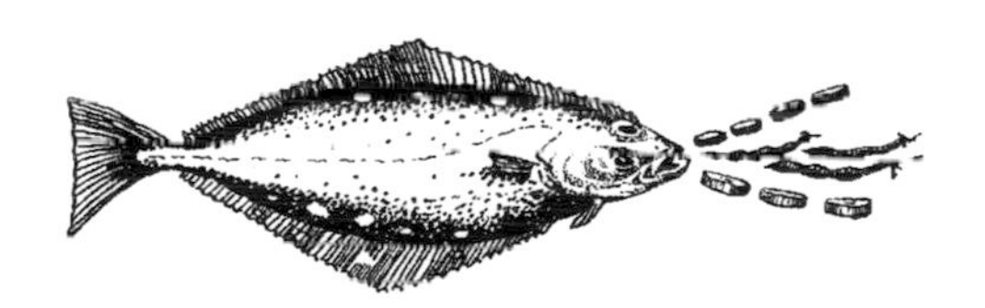

Lemon Dahl

serves 4

Lentils are not only protein rich but also have a high mineral and fibre content. They should be eaten in conjunction with grains in order to complete the amino acid chain and give a complete protein. The herbs and spices help to combat flatulence!

8 oz red lentils - ready cooked
1 large onion
1-2 tablespoons olive oil
2 fresh chillies deseeded and chopped
2 cloves garlic
1 teaspoon turmeric
2 teaspoons cumin seeds or 1 of powdered cumin
Juice of 1 lemon and 1 lime
A handful of fresh mint well chopped

Sauté the onion in olive oil for 5 mins and gradually add all the spices.
Cook together for further 5 mins.
Add the lentils and mint and cook again for 5 mins.
Add the lemon and lime slowly - tasting frequently to get the right flavour.

Serve with rice or millet to complete the protein and some green leafy vegetables.

Lentil Risotto *serves 4*

This dish combines lentils with rice and so completes the amino acid chain giving a complete protein. Lentils are not only an inexpensive form of wholesome nutritious food but they are easy and quick to cook, taking up the flavour of the herbs and garlic well and so this is a good standby dish.

1 large onion
3 cloves garlic
2 cups of brown rice
2 cups of water
Pinch of saffron
4 oz red lentils
$^1/_2$ pint water
Handful of fresh coriander

Chop the onion and garlic and sweat in a tablespoon of water in a pan for 5 mins. Add the rice and the 2 cups of water and bring to the boil and then simmer until all the water is absorbed. Add a pinch of saffron for colour. Separately cook the lentils in the half pint of water until they are soft and the water has been absorbed. Drain and mix with rice and oregano.

Serve with side salads.

Nut Burgers

makes 6

These are quick and easy to make and very satisfying to eat. Hazelnuts are a protein food with little oil content unlike other nuts. They have a strong flavour.

2 cups cooked brown rice
1 large onion
2 oz millet flakes
1 large grated carrot
4 oz hazelnuts
Handful of herbs (basil, oregano and coriander)

Chop onion and sweat in a tablespoon of water in a pan. Add the grated carrot and cook for a further 5 mins. Chop the nuts finely. Put cooked rice and millet flakes in bowl and using your hands work in the other ingredients then form burger shapes and cook in a medium oven for 20-30 mins.

Serve with stir fried vegetables or a large mix of salad ingredients.

Nut Roast

serves 6-8

Nuts are an excellent source of protein and this dish blends those which are oily with those which are least oily. Their oils help to provide the essential fatty acids which we require. Nuts are rich in potassium, zinc and magnesium and have strong flavours. This dish can be used as a substantial main course - it is quite filling.

1 dessertspoon olive oil
2 large onions
1 head celery
1/2 pint vegetable stock
1/2 handful each of fresh thyme and parsley
Juice of 2 lemons and their rinds
8 oz ground almonds or hazelnuts
8 oz chopped or broken cashews
4 oz millet flakes (or enough to keep the mixture smooth and not too runny)

Sauté onions and celery. Add stock. Simmer for 5 mins. Take off heat and stir in herbs and lemon. Cool slightly and stir in nuts and millet flakes. Grease tin and put in mixture. Put in hot oven for about half an hour and then turn out of tin.

Serve with a green salad and new potatoes.

Parsnip & Leek Frittata *serves 4*

Leeks are rich in potassium and like their cousins the onions and garlics have valuable cleansing properties. They are easy to grow if you have a vegetable garden as they need little attention. Use the whole leek as the stalks give colour to the dish. Parsnips have a strong texture which gives the frittata body and their distinctive flavour is compelling.

1 lb parsnips
8 oz leeks
1 tablespoon olive oil
6 organic free range eggs
Juice of 1 lemon
Handful fresh dill
1 teaspoon cayenne pepper

Grate the parsnips and simmer for about 10 mins in the lemon juice and a little water - be careful not to burn. This should cook using up the liquid but drain the parsnips and reserve the liquid in case you need it later. Meanwhile chop the leeks into small rounds and fry in the oil. Beat the eggs well with the dill, cayenne and mix in the leeks and parsnips.

Heat a frying pan and smear slightly with oil and when hot pour in the mixture cutting a figure of eight over it with a spatula until it sets. This will take about 8-10 mins. Then brown off the top under a grill or place the pan in a hot oven.

Serve either hot or cold with a large mixed salad.

Peasant Stew

serves 4-6

A Feast for a King!

This is my favourite recipe for feeding a large crowd of people. It seems to be very popular with all age groups and can be prepared well in advance. It is helpful to make large quantities and freeze some for a rainy day when the house is full of people. Remember to cook the chickpeas well although they will get further cooking when the stew is assembled. If it is combined with rice then the amino acid chain is completed to form a complete protein.

1 red onion
1 large courgette
1/2 a head of celery
4 bay leaves
8 oz fine green beans
1 tablespoon olive oil
3 cloves chopped garlic
1/2 teaspoon paprika
1 tablespoon turmeric
1 yellow pepper
6 inch sprig of rosemary
1-2 pints of apple juice
12 oz dried chickpeas
1 teaspoon arrowroot

Soak chickpeas overnight. Drain and put in pan with fresh water and bring to boil. Cook for about 1 hour until soft or use pressure cooker (see pulse information).
Sauté veg in oil and garlic. Add the paprika, turmeric, bay leaves and rosemary. Cook until soft.

Add the liquid slowly; keeping the consistency moist whilst making the sauce. Add the drained chickpeas and simmer for a few mins. If you like the sauce to be thicker add arrowroot as you add the liquid. Cook in medium oven for an hour or more. Remove rosemary and bay leaves.

Serve with brown rice and a mixed salad.
Corn bread is also delicious with this.

Pinekernel Roast

serves 4

Pinekernels have a pleasant rich nutty taste and they are a good source of protein, fat and carbohydrate. They are fairly oily and so blend well in cooking.

10 oz organic pinekernels
$^1/_2$ lb carrots
4 oz rice flour
2 organic free range eggs
1 large onion
Handful of fresh parsley

Coarsely grate the carrots and then place all ingredients in food mixer and mix thoroughly. Grease a 1 lb bread tin and pour mixture in and cook in a hot oven for about 30 mins. Cover initially and then remove covering in order to brown off the top. Turn out onto serving dish.

Serve with a watercress and tomato salad and brown rice.

Pulse Mix

serves 4 or more

Pulses are good forms of protein and should be served with grains to complete the amino acid chain. This mixture is extremely versatile for using as the basis for a soup or casserole. This is quick and easy as the pulses in this instance do not need to be pre soaked.

1 cup mung beans
1 cup yellow split peas
1 cup red lentils

This can be kept ready mixed in an airtight storage jar and then added to a soup or casserole as required.

To make a soup with this mixture try using the following.

2 medium onions
1 tablespoon olive oil
2 pts vegetable stock
4 oz pulse mix
1 heaped teaspoon rice miso

Finely chop onions and lightly fry in olive oil.
Add other ingredients and bring to boil for 5 mins and reduce to simmer until all pulses are well cooked and soft - approx 30 mins. For a casserole use less water which makes the dish thicker.

Serve soup with breads in the book or rice cakes.
Serve casseroles with rice, millet or buckwheat and vegetables.

Red Hot Bean Burgers *makes 4*

These burgers are very quick to make and can be altered according to whatever taste you prefer. i.e. If you want them to be really hot then use the chillies but if you prefer just a savoury taste then omit them and use the herbs on their own. Fresh herbs certainly give a much more pleasant flavour. These are popular with kids who of course love the shapes of burgers. The kidney beans give them a good colour. Chillies are said to benefit the heart and circulatory systems and to improve a sluggish digestive system and to help clear mucous from the respiratory tract.

8 oz kidney beans
$^3/_4$ lb potatoes
1 large onion
3 cloves garlic
1 teaspoon dried oregano or handful of fresh
2 dried chillies
1 tablespoon gramflour
1 dessertspoon olive oil

Soak and cook kidney beans according to pulses information. Be sure to cook them thoroughly. Boil potatoes separately. Combine all ingredients in a mixer and then shape into burgers.
Use a little of the flour to coat the burgers.
Bake in oven for a further 20 mins.

Serve with brown rice or millet and a salad.

Spanish Omelette *serves 4*

This quick and colourful dish makes a wonderful supper - it can be halved for a smaller number or doubled for a larger number. Any vegetables you have may be used but this combination gives an attractive appetising meal.
Eggs are rich in zinc and Vit B and they are a good source of protein.
Broccoli which is included in this dish is rich in iron and Vit C. Carrots give us good supplies of beta carotene and thus act as an anti oxidant. Leeks and onions have anti biotic properties and help boost the immune system. Kale like other green leafy vegetables is rich in calcium, potassium and iron.

4 organic free range eggs
1 head of broccoli
4 medium carrots
2 red onions
4 tablespoons Yofu
2 medium leeks
1 handful of curly kale
1 tablespoon olive oil

Chop all the vegetables except the kale into bite size pieces and lightly stir fry them in the olive oil for 10 mins in a large stainless steel frying pan. Meanwhile mix the eggs and yofu in a bowl with a blender until they resemble a cloudy mixture and add 4 tablespoons of water. Remove the kale from its stalks and chop it into strips and add this to the stir fry for a further 2 mins and then pour the egg mixture onto the vegetables. Make sure the egg sets and then cooks - this will take about 4-5 mins. Then place the frying pan under the grill for 2 mins to brown the top slightly.

To serve cut the omelette into four and place on warmed plates with a side salad.

Stuffed Cabbage Leaves *serves 4*

Cabbage which is rich in chlorophyll has been at the forefront of research concerning its properties to help prevent fatal diseases such as cancer and heart disease. It is extremely versatile and any type is beneficial. The lentils and rice in this dish combined will give good protein intake.

1 large red cabbage
1 large carrot
4 oz red lentils
4 oz pye lentils
$^1/_2$ handful chopped parsley
1 onion
6 oz cooked brown rice
1 organic free range egg

Thoroughly wash the lentils and cover them with water and bring to the boil and then simmer for about 20-30 mins until soft. Drain and keep warm. Reserve the cooking water incase it is needed for binding. Meanwhile finely chop the onion and carrots and sweat them in half a cup of water until tender and then combine with the lentils and cooked rice. Beat the egg and add this to the mixture. Carefully pull the larger leaves from the cabbage and thoroughly wash them. Place them in a pan with two tablespoons of water and lightly cook them for approx 2-3 mins. Fill the cabbage leaves with the mixture and place in baking dish and put in moderate oven for about 20 mins. Remove and decorate with chopped parsley. Use the inner leaves of the cabbage to make a salad.

Serve with salad.

Stuffed Marrow

serves 4-6

When courgettes become marrows they are a very useful and colourful vegetable. This dish could also be cooked in individual courgettes but the marrow adds splendour. If you grow your own then you can pick out the precise marrow for this dish; otherwise give it a tap on the side to ensure it is not too old and "woody". If it is it will sound hollow and some of the moisture will have dried up.

1 x 2-3 lb marrow
2 large onions
1 clove garlic
2 celery sticks
6 oz hazelnuts
Handful fresh parsley
2 cups brown rice
2 cups water

Cut the marrow in half and take out the seeds. Cook the rice in the water until all the liquid is absorbed. Sweat the finely chopped onions in a little water for 5 mins and add the chopped garlic and celery. Chop the hazelnuts into small pieces. Then in a bowl mix the cooked rice, nuts and onion mixture well and add the finely chopped parsley. Stuff both sides of the marrow and tie together with string. Place in a greased baking dish and arrange any left over stuffing around the outisde. Cover the entire dish and cook in a medium oven for about 45 mins (keep looking) until the marrow is tender. When ready remove covering and string and serve.

This is extremely colourful with the green skin of the marrow still retaining its hue. Cut into one inch slices and serve on its own or with a small salad and perhaps a carrot coulis.

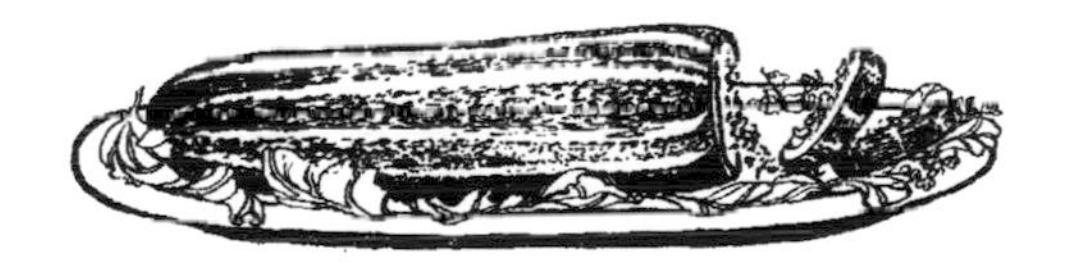

Vegetable Paella *serves 6*

A most useful dish where you can use either fresh vegetables or whatever you have in the fridge. Its a fabulous family meal and has a splendid aroma. Rice is recommended for digestive disorders and is a great eliminator as it gathers toxins on its travels through the Gastro Intestinal tract. The vegetables give helpful mineral wealth to the diet and the whole meal is full of fibre.

1 $^{1}/_{2}$ cups short grain brown rice
1 tablespoon olive oil
2 large carrots
1 head broccoli
1 head celery
juice of half a lemon
1 large onion
4 cloves garlic
1 yellow/red pepper or half of each
Large handful green french beans
3 - 4 cups vegetable stock or water
Large handful fresh basil

Sauté the onion and garlic in oil for about 10 mins using a Wok
Add the rice and stir well
Add the lemon juice
Add the stock (twice the quantity of water as rice)
bring to boil and simmer for about 30 mins with lid on
Chop up all the vegetables into bite size pieces
place them on top of the rice and cover – leave to simmer slowly for about 30-40 mins

Serve in the Wok whilst hot when all the moisture has been absorbed.
Sprinkle with chopped basil.

Vegetables with Crunchy Crumble Topping

serves many

This dish is so versatile - use whichever vegetables are available and adjust the amount according to the number of people you are feeding. Just fill your dish accordingly. Root vegetables are recommended for joint mobility and they are known as eliminators of uric acid. Carrots are rich in beta carotene and have high anti oxidant properties.
Oats are rich in Vit E, Vit B complex along with calcium, potassium and magnesium so together with the pumpkin and sunflower seeds which are rich in zinc and essential oils they add to a remarkably nutritious meal.

Swede, turnip, parsnip, carrots, onion and celery.
You'll need about 3 lbs of vegetables in all.

About 2 pints vegetable stock
About 2 teaspoonfuls arrowroot
A large sprig of fresh rosemary
1 tablespoon olive oil

For the crumble:

8 oz oats (coeliacs use 8 oz rice flour)
3 oz pumpkin seeds
3 oz sunflower seeds
1 -2 tablespoon olive oil

Peel, and cut the vegetables into bite size pieces. Sauté the vegetables in oil turning well. Add sprigs of rosemary. Cover and cook for up to 20 mins. Add stock slowly and fast simmer for 10 mins. Stir in enough arrowroot to thicken sauce - add more stock if needed. Transfer to ovenproof casserole dish. To make crumble topping: combine the dry ingredients and mix well. Rub in margarine or oil until mixture is a crumbly consistency. This is easily done in a mixer. Spread crumble over top of vegetables and bake in oven for about $^{1}/_{2}$ hour or until topping is brown.

Vegetarian Moussaka *serves 6-8*

This is a very versatile dish which can be prepared in advance. You'll be surprised how many people enjoy a second helping! The lentils have protein properties and it is best to serve with a grain. The aubergines absorb the seasonings and herbs well and the carrot juice keeps the whole dish moist and colourful.

4 oz puy lentils
4 oz red lentils
2 large onions
2 tablespoons olive oil
4 chopped garlic cloves
$^{1}/_{2}$ chopped fresh red pepper
3 medium carrots
Large handful chopped fresh basil
1 celery heart - chopped
1 litre organic carrot juice
Juice of half a lemon
2 aubergines
About 2 lbs potatoes
1 tablespoon olive oil

Fry the onions in the oil for about 5 mins. Add the lentils, garlic, pepper, carrots, basil and celery and stir over the heat for a couple of mins. Gradually add $^{3}/_{4}$ of the carrot and lemon juice and simmer for half an hour, occasionally stirring. The mixture will thicken as the lentils cook so add more of the carrot juice as and when required reserving a little for covering the base of the casserole dish. Mash the sauce with a potato masher to thicken it. Whilst this is cooking slice the aubergines thinly and set aside, peel and thinly slice the potatoes.

Cover the base of a casserole dish with carrot juice and then place a layer of aubergines over this. Cover with the lentil sauce and keep layering until all the sauce is used up. Finally cover the top with a layer of potatoes and drizzle the oil over the top for browning. Cook in moderate oven for 40 mins.

Serve with crisp green salad and a little millet or buckwheat.

VEGETABLE & GRAIN DISHES

Vegetables are a crucial part of a healthy diet. With the produce of the world at your doorstep and a wider range of organic vegetables on offer, there has never been a better time to experiment with new flavours, new combinations and new ways of serving nutritious meals that will do you a power of good. These dishes can be used either as main courses or as accompanying dishes.

Grains are another essential part of our diet and their inclusion as a base or accompaniment for vegetables or as part of the main dish is helpful.

Asparagus, Onion & Rocket Stirfry

serves 4

Asparagus always gives an exotic air to a meal. It is so simple to prepare and adds tremendous colour and texture. Make sure the tips are firm and slightly closed and not too fat as they aren't as tasty if they are too large. Asparagus is said to stimulate the liver and kidneys.

1 bundle asparagus (1-1$^1/_2$ lbs)
1 large red onion
2-3 handfuls rocket leaves
$^1/_2$ tablespoon olive oil
1 clove garlic

Peel the onion and garlic and chop them fairly finely. Wash the rocket and asparagus well, trimming any hard stalks from the asparagus - usually about 2-3 inches. (save for a soup). Sauté the onion and garlic in the oil for 5 mins stirring continuously and then add the asparagus, cooking it for about 5 mins, still stirring continuously and finally add the rocket and take the pan off the heat and stir it in. The flavour of this mixture is delicious.

Serve either on top of polenta or a bed of brown rice or on its own as a starter.

Coconut Rice

serves 4

This is a delicious alternative to plainly cooked rice. It makes the meal slightly more exotic and gives it an Asian flavour. Coconut is a rich protein.

2 cups short grain organic brown rice
2-3 cups water
8 oz creamed coconut
1 dessertspoon olive oil
1 onion
2 tablespoons chopped coriander

Chop the onion very finely and lightly fry it in the oil in a pan with the thoroughly washed rice for 4 mins. Boil the water and pour it over the creamed coconut in a jug and allow it to mix up into a milk and then pour it over the rice. Bring to the boil and either simmer for 25 mins on top of the cooker or put in a moderate oven for a similar time until all the liquid has been absorbed.

Serve with casseroles, vegetable dishes or fish. To enhance the flavour decorate with chopped coriander.

Colourful Eastern Vegetables

serves 4

This is a refreshingly bright tasty dish which looks good accompanying any fish, pulse or grain meal. It needs to be cooked immediately prior to eating to maintain its cheerful character.

2 handfuls mangetout
8 spring onions
2 inches fresh ginger
1 dessertspoon sherry
2 tablespoons pine kernels
1 dessertspoon olive oil

Lightly dry roast the pine kernels in a pan and reserve.
Chop the mangetout and spring onions into bite size pieces and lightly fry them in the olive oil.
Add the ginger and sherry and cook for a further five minutes.

Serve sprinkled with the pine kernels.

Herb Mash

serves 4

The potato is a very versatile friend. It provides a good volume of fibre, Vitamin B complex and Vitamin C. Try to cook in very little water so that the nutrients are not discarded. They are known for helping with the digestive tract.

3 lbs potatoes
1 tablespoon non hydrogenated margarine
2 tablespoons Yofu 'live' yoghurt
Large handful of garden parsley (or coriander or mint or chives)
Sprinkling of seaweed condiment

Boil the spuds until they are cooked right through in a very small amount of water so that they are almost steaming. Chop your chosen herb very well. Mash the spuds until they have a fine consistency and stir in the margarine, Yofu and herb. Add a little seaweed condiment - this adds to the colour as well as the flavour. This can be served with any meal or used as a basis and covered with stir fried vegetables.

Leek Bake

serves 4

Leeks are a member of the onion and garlic family and contain invaluable properties for clearing the sinuses. Eaten on a regular basis they are helpful for keeping infections away as they have strong antibiotic qualities. Good sized leeks are best in this dish so that they do not break up.

3 large leeks
1 carrot
$^1/_2$ lb broad beans
$^1/_2$ teaspoon cumin
$^1/_2$ teaspoon fenugreek
1 tablespoon olive oil
1 cup of carrot juice
$1^1/_2$ lbs potatoes
1 teaspoon arrowroot.

Chop the leeks in large one inch rounds using the green part as well. Also chop the carrot and fry both in oil. Add the broad beans, seasonings and carrot juice. Cook and stir for about 5 mins. Thicken if necessary with arrowroot. Place in ovenproof serving dish. Slice the potatoes and put on top drizzled with a little oil and bake in the oven for 30 mins. If preferred this dish can be topped with savoury crumble.

Serve either as a main dish or as a vegetable dish.

Mash with Red Onions *serves 4*

Potatoes give us good fibre and are rich in useful vitamins and minerals. This dish utilises their versatility in providing a base for the highly prized onion which gives us antibiotic qualities and has strong eliminatory powers. The colour differential provides an exotic looking but simple dish.

2 lbs potatoes
Water to cook potatoes
4 tablespoons rice milk
Handful fresh basil
4 Medium Red Onions
Sprinkling of seaweed

Place the onions in a covered dish and bake in a moderate oven for approx. 40 mins. Remove the outer layer of skin being careful to keep the onions whole. Meanwhile boil the potatoes in a little water and mash them to a smooth paste adding the rice milk. Chop the basil finely and stir in to the potato mixture. Place a portion of mash in the centre of a dinner plate and place the red onion on top and sprinkle with seaweed.

Serve as a main dish with other vegetables or a salad.

Polenta

serves 8

This is a staple food in Northern Italy - the thick savoury mixture is a basis for any vegetable dish. It is colourful and the texture is different from rice or millet.

8 oz polenta flour
2 pts water
1 teaspoon ruthmol

Place all ingredients in a pan and bring to the boil stirring constantly. As it comes to the boil continue to stir and then lower the heat. During the next 15 mins of cooking stir frequently whilst the mixture bubbles- it is ready when the porridge is firm and the spoon stands up in it. At this point flavourings can be mixed in. (Teaspoon Harissa, teaspoon powdered chilli, or some fresh herbs). Then pour the mixture into a greased dish at least 1 inch deep and leave to cool. The polenta will set like custard and can then be cut into squares, rounds or slices, baked in garlic oil and used as a base for vegetable dishes. Alternatively it can be mixed with flavourings or layered with different colours to give a sandwich effect.

Pumpkin Mash & Fine Beans

serves 4

Pumpkins are full of betacarotene which is recommended for improved circulation, respiratory problems, heart disease and cancer prevention. It is also said to rejuvenate the skin. This is an attractive dish, easy to make and tasty.

4 lb pumpkin
1 teaspoon nutmeg
$^1/_2$ cup rice milk
8 oz green french beans
2 cloves garlic
$^1/_2$ teaspoon paprika

Wash the pumpkin and remove the seeds and place it covered in a moderate oven to bake for about $^3/_4$ hour. When soft scoop all the flesh away from the skin and mash it well adding the rice milk and nutmeg. Meanwhile steam the beans for approx. 5 mins with the well crushed garlic. Place portions of the pumpkin mash onto individual plates and pile the beans over the top. Sprinkle with paprika.

Serve with other vegetables, fish, burgers, lentil dishes or salads.

Ragout of Vegetables

serves 4

The herb "mint" has been recognised as a helpful digestive aid for many years and is widely used in the Middle and Far East in general cookery. It has a distinctive flavour and is also colourful. There are several varieties and growing mint in the garden and picking it to use fresh is most rewarding.

- $^1/_2$ lb carrots
- $^1/_2$ small white turnips
- 1 handful fresh mint (from the garden if possible)
- $^1/_2$ lb new potatoes
- $^1/_4$ lb french beans
- Bunch of spring onions
- 2 handfuls of peas or broad beans
- 1 pint of vegetable stock or water or carrot juice or mixture of all.
- 1 tablespoon olive oil
- 1 tablespoon cornflour or arrowroot

Chop the onions, carrots and turnips into bite size pieces and put into pan with oil for about 5 mins. Stir well. Meanwhile in a bowl blend a little stock with the cornflour to form a paste and gradually add the rest of the stock. Add the potatoes to the pan and then gradually stir in the cornflour mixture. Add the other vegetables and the well chopped mint and transfer to an oven proof casserole dish and cook in a slow oven for 3 - 4 hours.

The mint gives this casserole a very definite flavour. You can use alternative vegetables but try to keep it colourful.

Serve on its own or with rice.

Ratatouille

serves 4

This colourful vegetable dish has a distinctive Mediterranean look about it.
Onions and garlic are recommended to us for their cleansing properties and they always give good flavour to vegetable dishes. Carrot juice is a beneficial aid for the liver and its inclusion here gives this dish a completely different appearance from traditional ratatouille.

1 yellow pepper
$^1/_2$ pt carrot juice
1 lb courgettes
1 large onion (preferably red)
3 cloves garlic
1 large carrot
1 tablespoon chopped parsley

Roughly chop onion, garlic and pepper. Sweat them in a tablespoon of carrot juice for 3 mins and then add the pepper. Chop carrot and courgette into inch size pieces and add them and cook for a further 8 mins. Add the carrot juice and continue cooking for about another 8 mins or until all the vegetables are tender. Stir in the parsley at the very end and only cook for a minute.

Serve as a main vegetable dish or to accompany other dishes or simply with rice. I make up large batches of this and then freeze various sizes of portions. Ratatouille is also splendid served over a portion of polenta.

Rice

serves 4

This is a tremendously versatile food which has been a major part of the diet in the Far and Middle East for years. It should however be eaten in its true unpolished state as organic brown rice. It is a complete food and is helpful for cleansing the digestive tract and driving out toxins. It can be served with any dish either hot or cold. This quantity is for a four person serving but it is fine to cook larger amounts when making a main meal and keep them in the fridge so as to have some at hand for snacks or lunches.

2 cups short grain organic brown rice
2-3 cups water
Tiny drop olive oil

Wash the rice thoroughly and then place in either an ovenproof dish which can also be used on the top of the cooker or a normal saucepan. Add the water and bring to the boil. Drizzle in the oil (which prevents the rice sticking) and either leave to simmer for 25 mins on the top or place in a moderate oven for a similar time until all the moisture has been absorbed. If you wish the rice to be chewy then use 2 cups of water but if you wish it to be softer then make it 3 cups of water.

Serve with any of the casseroles, main meals or vegetable dishes.

Risotto of Onion and Garlic *serves 4*

This is another variation using the ever versatile brown rice. It is recommended for calming and cleansing the gastro intestinal tract and has for years been advocated as useful for lowering high blood pressure. The antibacterial and circulatory properties of the garlic and onion used here makes this dish extremely valuable for health. Use it regularly and appreciate the wealth of goodness as you eat.

2 cups brown rice
2 $^1/_2$ cups vegetable stock
3 large red onions
4-5 garlic cloves depending on size
1 tablespoons olive oil
Handful of fresh basil

Finely chop the onions, garlic and basil.
Sauté them all in the oil and after about 6 mins leave to keep warm but off the heat. Put the rice in the vegetable stock and leave to simmer for 30 mins or until all the water is absorbed. Stir the onion mixture into the rice and cook for a couple of mins and then turn into serving dish.

Serve with any of the vegetable dishes or a fresh leafy salad.

Roasted Mix Veg

serves 4-6

This exotic tasting dish turns many a head because it is so attractive with such a splash of colour. It is very quick and simple to make.

3 courgettes
1 large aubergine
1 yellow pepper
1 onion
2 tablespoons olive oil
juice of half a lemon
4 garlic cloves
grated rind from half a lemon
parsley

Mix grated lemon rind, chopped garlic, juice of lemon and olive oil together.
Chop parsley and reserve.

Chop courgettes in wide rounds, chop aubergines in large chunks and chop pepper in thumb size pieces. Place veg in roasting dish and pour over the oil and juice mixture. Place in hot oven for approx 20 - 30 mins and baste when necessary.

When veg are cooked serve over a bed of rice or millet and sprinkle with chopped parsley.

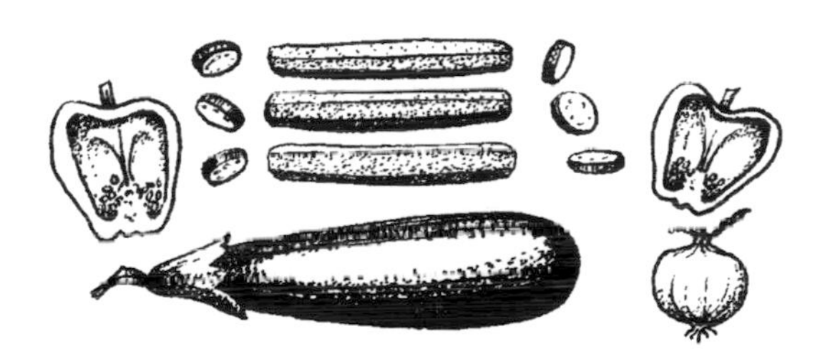

Saag

serves 4

This Indian dish can be used as an extra vegetable when serving pulses or rice. Spinach is very rich in iron and in order to retain its nutrients it should be cooked in just the water left on the leaves after washing. Being a dark green leafy vegetable its nutrients also include magnesium and calcium and cancer fighting carotenoids.

2 lb fresh spinach
1 large onion - chopped
4 cloves garlic
1 tablespoon olive oil
2 oz freshly grated ginger
$^{1}/_{2}$ teaspoon ground nutmeg
1 teaspoon crushed coriander seeds
1 teaspoon ground cumin
1 deseeded and chopped green chilli
1 teaspoon chopped fresh coriander
dash of paprika

Wash the spinach very well, strip the leaves from the stalks, drain and lightly shred the leaves and set aside.
Fry the onion and garlic in the olive oil in a pan for about 4 mins.
Add the ginger, coriander seeds, cumin and nutmeg and cook for another 5 mins on low heat with lid on.
Add the spinach and chilli and cook on low heat with lid on for about 4-5 mins until spinach is well wilted.

Put in serving dish and sprinkle with chopped fresh coriander and a dash of paprika.

Steaming Hot Vegetables *serves 4-6*

The wealth of nutritious vitamin and mineral content in these vegetables makes this dish a weekly necessity. These vegetables have helpful qualities to perhaps ward off infection, protect us against fatal diseases, assist our joints and support our skin and eyes.

2 red onions
8 medium carrots
1 head broccoli
1 head cauliflower
2 courgettes
2 parsnips
1 pt water
pinch of seaweed condiment and ruthmol

Peel the onions and halve. Scrape the carrots, peel the parsnips, wash the courgettes and chop them all into bite size pieces. Wash and split the heads of cauliflower and broccoli into large pieces and chop up the stalks into smaller bite size pieces. Pour the water into the lower pan of a steamer and put all the vegetables into the upper pan adding pinch of seaweed and ruthmol. Put the upper pan on top of the water pan and bring the water to the boil and then simmer for about 6 8 minutes - testing to see if the vegetables are soft enough. Remove from heat and place attractively in a serving dish. Sprinkle with seaweed condiment. Keep the precious water to add to soups, sauces or casseroles. Some of the nutrients will have been leached into the water - it makes a tasty drink.

Serve with rice, fish, burgers etc and/or with a sauce or dressing.

Stir Fried Mixed Vegetables *serves 4*

This method of cooking is excellent for sealing in the juices and it takes such a short time - dinner is ready in a flash. This dish is full of valuable nutrients and also gives plenty of fibre from the large selection of vegetables.

1 onion
4 cloves garlic
1 inch ginger
1 tablespoon olive oil
2 sticks celery
1 handful mangetout
1 handful green beans
$^{1}/_{4}$ cauliflower
$^{1}/_{4}$ broccoli
2 large carrots
$^{1}/_{2}$ fennel
1 leek
1 handful sprouted chickpeas
1handful sprouted mung beans
1 courgette

Sauté the roughly chopped onion and garlic in the oil for 4 mins. Coarsely chop the celery, carrots, broccoli, cauliflower and fennel and add them and cook for further 5 mins stirring all the time. Cut the leek into rounds and the beans into thirds and add these and the mangetout for further 4 mins.
Grate and add the ginger, chickpeas, mung beans and sliced courgette and continuing stirring and cooking for a further 5 mins. The vegetables should be crunchy and full of flavour. If at any time they stick in the pan then either add a tablespoon of water or put the lid on but when you do this they will become softer.

Serve with fish, rice or any main dish.

Stuffed Jackets

serves 4

As most of the nutritious value including potassium is found in the skin of the potato this is a simple way to provide a highly healthy meal giving good fibre content and vital minerals and vitamins.

4 medium sized potatoes weighing about 8-10 oz each

Thoroughly wash and scrub the potatoes and prick the skins with a fork well into the flesh in about 6-8 places. Place in a medium oven for approximately $^3/_4$ of an hour. Test to see if the potatoes are cooked throughout by piercing them with a knife. When ready remove from oven and cut each potato across to almost half it and then across the other way and push the sides together to create a slight puffed opening.

Any of the following could be used as a filling: Asparagus Onion & Rocket Stirfry, Avocado Pate, All the Salads, Coleslaw, Colourful Eastern Veg, Mayonnaise, Pesto, Ratatouille, Ragout of Veg, Roasted Mixed Veg, Saag, Salsa or Stir Fried Mixed Veg. Put the baked potato on a plate, slit the top open and pile the filling on top so that some of it spills over the sides. Enjoy!

Stuffed Pumpkin

serves 4-6

The colourful pumpkin is rich in beta carotene. We need plenty of this to help protect against cancer, circulatory and respiratory problems. This is a very warming dish and is a welcome alternative in the Autumn when the root vegetables tend to be paler colours. It can also be used for a light lunch and goes a long way so can feed an unexpected crowd.

1 cup shortgrain brown rice
8 oz red onions
3 cloves garlic
1 medium sized pumpkin
1 tablespoons olive oil
1 large handful green beans
8 spring onions
8 oz sprouts (usually chickpeas and lentils)
juice of half a lemon
A large handful of fresh basil

Take the top off the pumpkin, remove the seeds and place it in a warm oven to loosen the flesh. (approx 20 mins). Cook the rice as per grains guidelines. Meanwhile roast the chopped red onions, green beans and sprouts in oil for about 15 mins. Add the sliced spring onions just for a few mins.
When pumpkin has cooked a little remove the flesh and combine with other veg and then mix with rice. Add chopped basil and garlic and return to middle of pumpkin. Bake in moderate oven for 15 mins to warm through.

This dish is very appetising because of its unique colour. Serving it in the pumpkin case replacing the top brings an element of surprise to the table!

Vegetable Stock

1 large onion
4 medium carrots
2 cloves garlic
Any broccoli stalks, outside cabbage leaves, trimmings
 from vegetables including lettuce.
1 tablespoon olive oil
Handful fresh herbs of any kind or mixture of what
you have. (not mint)
2 pts water
Ruthmol and seaweed to taste

Sauté chopped garlic, onion and carrots for 5 mins. Add any other ingredients and water and bring to boil and then simmer for about an hour. Strain and use in soups, stews, casseroles or sauces.

INDEX

Notes

Notes

Notes